LOOK ■ AROUND ■ YOU

THE
CLOTHES
WE WEAR

Sally Hewitt and Jane Rowe

Evans

Evans Brothers Limited

About this book

This book has been put together in a way that makes it ideal for teachers and parents to share with young children. Take time over each question and project. Have fun learning about how all sorts of different homes, and the objects in them, have been designed for a special purpose.

The Clothes We Wear deals with the kinds of ideas about design and technology that many children will be introduced to in their early years at school. The pictures and text will encourage children to explore design on the page, and all around them. This will help them to understand some of the basic rules about why items of clothing are made from particular materials and are a certain shape, and why they are suited to certain occasions and are easy to wear. It will also help them to develop their own design skills.

The 'Eye-opener' boxes reveal interesting and unusual facts, or lead children to examine one particular aspect of design. There are also activities that put theory into practice in an entertaining and informative way. Children learn most effectively by joining in, talking, asking questions and solving problems, so encourage them to talk about what they are doing and to find ways of solving the problems for themselves.

Try to make thinking about design and technology a part of everyday life. Just pick up any object around the house and talk about why it has been made that way, and how it could be improved. Design is not just a subject for adults. You can have a lot of fun with it at any age – and develop both artistic flair and practical skills.

Contents

The clothes we wear **6**

Different materials **8**

Keeping cool **10**

Keeping warm and dry **12**

Sportsgear **14**

Clothes for protection **16**

Clothes to work in **18**

Make a waistcoat **20**

Shoes **22**

Soles **24**

Clothes from around the world **26**

Amazing designs **28**

Index **30**

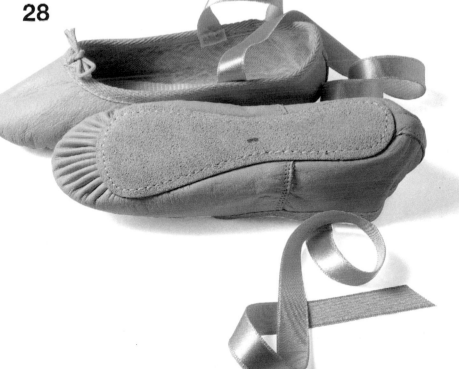

The clothes we wear

Every morning, you choose what clothes
you are going to wear and then
get dressed for the day.

Look at the clothes Nick
and Ellie are wearing.

Where do you think they are going?
Do you think they are going to the same place?
What do you think they will be doing?
Can you guess what Ellie's favourite colour is?
What clothes did you put on this morning?

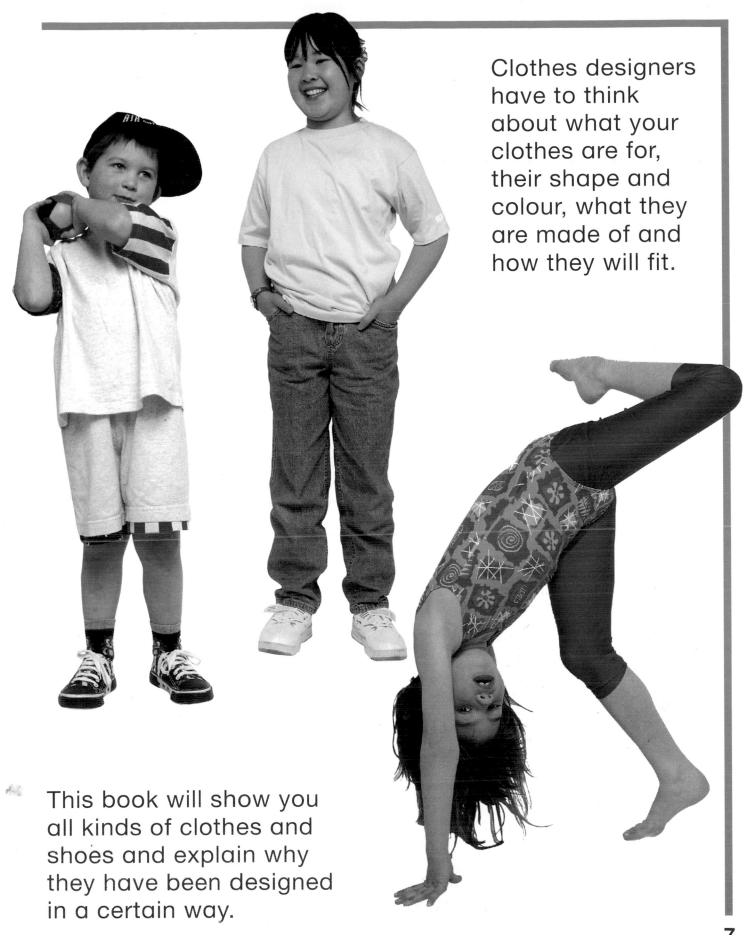

Clothes designers have to think about what your clothes are for, their shape and colour, what they are made of and how they will fit.

This book will show you all kinds of clothes and shoes and explain why they have been designed in a certain way.

Different materials

Feel the clothes you are wearing. Do they feel soft, rough or silky? Materials can come from animals or plants, or they may be man made.

sheep's wool

ball of wool

Wool
Most wool comes from sheep. Some comes from goats, llamas and rabbits! It is soft and warm.

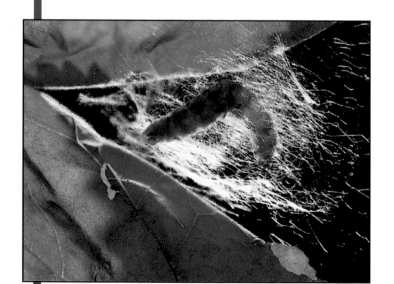

silk worm at work

Silk
Silk feels very light and smooth. It is made from the cocoon spun by silk worms!

8

Cotton and linen

Cotton and linen come from plants.
Linen is from the flax plant
and is very strong and tough.

flax plant

cotton plant

linen

close-
up of
material

Polyester and nylon come from oil!

Chemicals from oil are used to make
a special kind of plastic, which is
squeezed through tiny holes to make
threads.

nylon

polyester

9

Keeping cool

Your clothes help to keep you the right temperature.

These clothes have been specially designed to keep you cool in hot weather.

A hat with a brim protects your head from the sun.

Cotton clothes help to keep you cool.

The air can keep your feet cool when you wear open sandals.

Would you rather wear tight or loose clothes in hot weather?

Why do you think people wear light coloured clothes in hot weather?

Leave a dark and light coloured T-shirt in the sun for ten minutes and then feel them.

What do you notice? Which one would you rather wear on a hot day?

Eye-opener

People in hot countries often wear long, loose robes to protect them from the sun.

Air moves around inside the robes and helps to keep them cool.

Keeping warm and dry

These clothes will help to keep you warm and dry in cold or wet weather.

A lot of heat from your body escapes through your head.

A warm hat helps to keep your whole body warm.

This padded coat keeps you warm – just like a duvet!

What can you see that is made of wool?

This coat is waterproof. Raindrops roll off the shiny material.

What else is Chloe wearing that is waterproof?

Can you see anything on these two pages that would keep you both warm and dry?

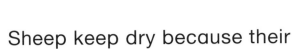
Sheep keep dry because their woolly coats are oily as well as soft and warm.

This coat is made of material that has been rubbed with oil to make it waterproof.

surface of material

Sportsgear

There are specially designed clothes and shoes for every different sport.

Cyclists wear helmets to protect their heads in case they have an accident.

Fluorescent colours glow in car headlights, so that the cyclist can be spotted easily in the dark.

Cycling gloves have leather palms for gripping the handlebars firmly.

Why do you think cyclists wear tight and stretchy shorts?

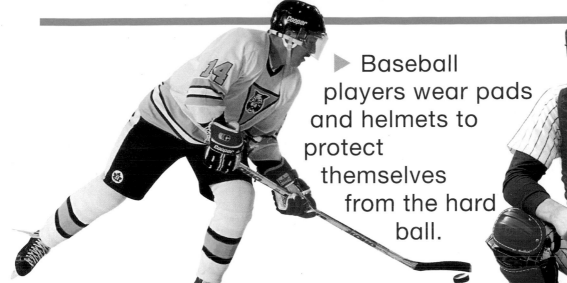

▶ Baseball players wear pads and helmets to protect themselves from the hard ball.

▲ An ice-hockey goalkeeper wears a helmet to protect his head from the hard puck.

▶ A fencer can see through the metal mesh of a fencing mask, but a foil cannot pierce it.

Eye-opener

In the early part of this century, women covered up well when they went swimming.

Modern swimsuits are designed for speeding through the water.

Clothes for protection

Some clothes and shoes have been specially designed to protect people while they work.

Why do you think a building site worker must always wear a hard hat?

Builders' boots have tough soles and steel-capped toes.

Surgeons have to keep very clean to protect their patients from germs.

Hats completely cover their hair.

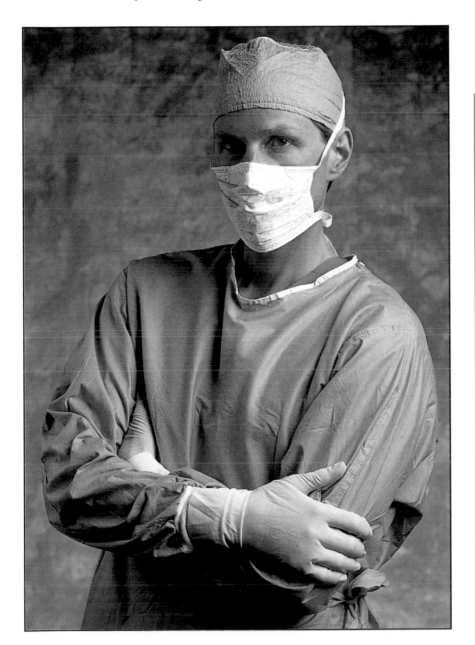

Eye-opener

Surgeons use their hands for very delicate work, so their gloves have to fit like a second skin.

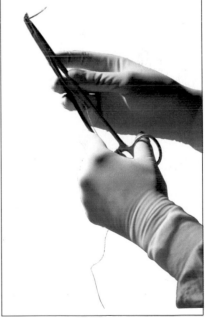

Why do you think they wear a mask over their nose and mouth?

Can you guess what kind of shoes they wear in the operating theatre?

Clothes to work in

You can often guess what kind of work someone does because of the clothes they wear.

Fishermen wear waterproof clothes to keep them completely dry in stormy seas.

Look through the book to find some more clothes made of waterproof material.

When there has been a fire, fire fighters rush to help.

Why do you think they wear brightly coloured strips that reflect the light?

A track suit allows a sports teacher to move around easily and keeps her warm when she is standing still.

Humans cannot survive in space, so a space suit has to be designed for an astronaut to live in. It is airtight and made of strong layers of plastic.

An oxygen tank gives the astronaut air to breathe.

Make a waistcoat

1 First, get someone to measure your chest size with a tape measure. Add a few centimetres to allow for the seams of the waistcoat.

2 Now divide this figure into 2. This is how big the back of your waistcoat should be. The front is the same size, only it is cut into 2 pieces.

3 Cut out your material in pieces like the ones shown below. You might like to try first with paper and then pin your paper pieces to your material and cut around them. Get a grown-up to help you with the pins and cutting.

4 Now sew the pieces together. Backstitch is a good stitch to use.

5 Do you want ribbon ties or buttons? If you want buttons, make button holes by cutting slits and then sewing over the edges with blanket stitch to stop them from fraying.

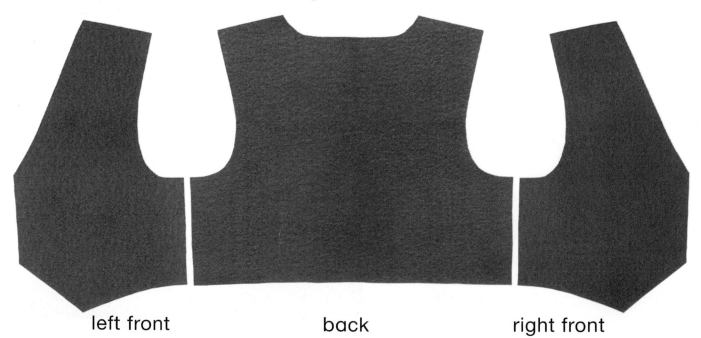

left front   back   right front

Can you see where blanket stitch has been used?

What ways can you think of to decorate
your waistcoat?

What other shapes and styles can you think of?

Shoes

Imagine going to school without your shoes on!

Shoes protect your feet and should be comfortable to wear.

Would all the shoes you can see here be as good as these trainers for running around in?

Leather is good for making shoes because it is tough, bends easily and lets air through to your feet.

Which of these shoes would be the fastest to put on?

◀ These boots are warm and waterproof and very light to wear in the snow.

▶ Why do you think flip-flops are good to wear when you are playing on the beach?

Eye-opener

Clogs are carved from wood to fit the shape of your foot.

Do you think they are comfortable to wear?

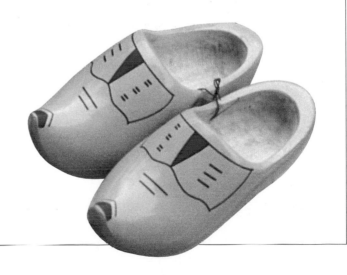

Soles

The sole is the part of your shoe that leaves a footprint.

▶ The sole of this walking boot can grip on wet, rough or slippery ground.

◀ Thick soles filled with air make the hard ground feel softer as you run along.

► Football boots have screw-in studs.

What would happen if you played football on wet grass without studs on your boots?

◄ The soles of wellies are sealed onto the boot so that you can splash in puddles and keep your feet dry!

► Thin leather soles stop the ballerina slipping as she dances.

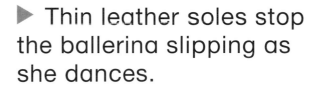

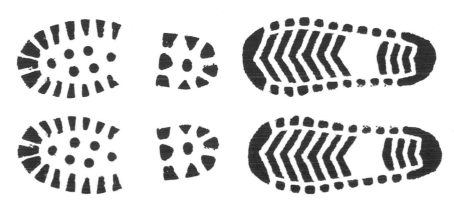

◄ Match each shoe to the footprint it has made.

Clothes from around the world

The ideas for the design of these modern clothes and shoes have come from all over the world.

A sarong comes from Malaysia. It is made from one piece of cloth wrapped around your body.

Try wrapping a long piece of material around your body in different ways.

Hard-wearing denim jeans were made for American gold diggers over a hundred years ago.

Next time you go out, count how many people you can see wearing jeans!

▶ Native Americans first made moccasins from animal skins.

Can you see how these slippers are similar to moccasins?

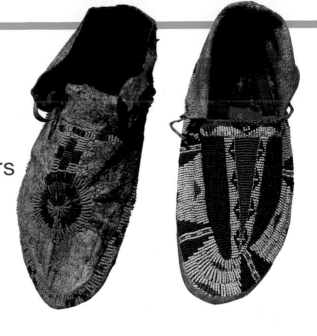

Eye-opener

You can get all kinds of hats for sunny weather.

This is a special kind called a Panama hat.

Real Panama hats are made from leaves of the panama hat palm! They are made so that you can roll them up tightly.

27

Amazing designs

All these clothes have been designed to be worn, but look how imaginative the designers have been with their ideas, shapes and materials!

▶ This fish-shaped watch is unusual and good fun. What other animals would make good shapes for a watch?

▼ What do you think this is supposed to be?
If you aren't sure, the answer is on page 30.

▲ Do you think you could run to catch a bus or walk to school in these shoes?

▶These trousers are so enormous that you and a friend could fit in the legs!

▼ But when they are worn like this, by an adult, they look perfectly normal and stylish.

Which of these clothes would you like to wear? What would you change about them?

Think about the design of the clothes you wear and all the clothes you see around you every day.

29

Index

astronaut 19

baseball 15
boots 16, 23, 24, 25
builder 16

cool, keeping 10-11, 27
cotton 9, 10
cycling 14

dry, keeping 13

fencing 15
fire fighter 18
fisherman 18
flax plant 9

hats 10, 12, 16, 17, 27, 28

ice hockey 15

jeans 26

linen 9

moccasins 27

nylon 9

Panama hat 27
platform shoes 28
polyester 9

sarong 26
sheep 8, 13
shoes 10, 22-23, 27, 28
silk 8
soles of shoes 24-25
surgeon 17
swimming 15

trousers 29

waistcoast, making a 20-21
warm, keeping 12, 19
watch 28
waterproof clothes 13, 18, 23
wool 8, 12

Answer to page 28:
The mysterious object is a hat!